CogAT® Practice Test Multilevel Battery — Levels E and F

Illustrations by: Kenneth Sommer
Written and published by: Bright Kids NYC

Bright Kids NYC Inc.
www.brightkidsnyc.com
info@brightkidsnyc.com
917-539-4575

About Bright Kids NYC

Bright Kids NYC was founded in New York City to provide language arts and math enrichment for young children, and to educate parents about standardized tests through workshops and consultations, as well as to prepare young children for such tests through assessments, tutoring, and publications. Our philosophy is that regardless of age, test-taking is a skill that can be acquired and mastered through practice.

At Bright Kids NYC, we strive to provide the best learning materials. Our publications are truly unique. First, all of our books have been created by qualified psychologists, learning specialists, and teachers. Second, our books have been tested by hundreds of children in our tutoring practice. Since children can make associations that many adults cannot, testing of materials by children is critical to creating successful test preparation guides. Finally, our learning specialists and teaching staff have provided practical strategies and tips so that parents can prepare their children to succeed on standardized tests.

Feel free to contact us should you have any questions.

Bright Kids NYC Inc.
225 Broadway
Suite 3104
New York, New York 10007

Phone: 917-539-4575
Email: info@brightkidsnyc.com
www.brightkidsnyc.com
www.twitter.com/brightkids

CogAT® Practice Test – Levels E and F   Bright Kids NYC Inc ©

Introduction

Bright Kids NYC created the *CogAT®* Practice Test to familiarize children with the content and the format of the *CogAT®*. Children, no matter how bright they are, do not always perform well when they are not accustomed to the format and the structure of a test. Children can misunderstand the directions, fail to look at all the answer choices, and may not always listen carefully to the questions. Thus, without adequate preparation and familiarization, children may not always perform to the best of their ability on standardized tests such as the *CogAT®*.

This Bright Kids *CogAT®* Practice Test is not designed to generate a score or a stanine as the test has not been standardized with the actual *CogAT®* norms and standards. The objective of the practice test is to identify your child's strengths and weaknesses and test taking ability so that you can prepare your child adequately for the actual test.

In order to maximize the effectiveness of the Bright Kids *CogAT®* Practice Test, it is important to first familiarize yourself with the test and its instructions. In addition, it is recommended that you designate a quiet place to work with your child, ideally in a neutral environment free of noise and clutter. Finally, provide a comfortable and proper seating arrangement to enable your child to focus and concentrate to the best of his or her ability.

Children will be taking many standardized tests throughout their school years. Teaching your child critical thinking skills along with test taking strategies at a young age will benefit your child for many years to come. Our philosophy is that regardless of age, test-taking is a skill than can be acquired and mastered through practice.

CogAT® Practice Test – Levels E and F Bright Kids NYC Inc ©

CogAT® Overview

The Cognitive Abilities Test® (most commonly known as the *CogAT®*) is designed to evaluate the level and pattern of cognitive development of students in grades K through 12. It is important to note that the *CogAT®* measures developed abilities, not innate abilities. The development of these abilities begins at birth and continues through early adulthood and is vastly influenced by both in-school and out-of-school life experiences. Since these abilities are closely related to an individual's success in school, test results may be used in combination with other relevant information to adapt instruction in order to enchance successful learning and to help identify children who may belong in Gifted and Talented programs.

The *CogAT®* is based on concepts drawn from several theoretical models of human abilities, but is primarily based on Vernon's (1961) hierarchical model and Cattell's (1987) fluid-crystallized model. In brief, both models have the factor G, or general reasoning ability, and consider it as the essential organizing cognitive construct that plays a central role in all learning and problem solving. In the *CogAT®*, G is operationally defined as abstract reasoning skills with special emphasis on inductive reasoning that is fundamental for acquiring knowledge, organizing it, and storing it in memory. Vernon's and Cattell's models also provide four major group factors which Vernon calls verbal educational abilities and Cattell calls crystallized abilities. In the *CogAT®*, the Verbal and Quantitative batteries appraise some of the abilities in these clusters. The clusters become much more differentiated and more closely related to specific kinds of learning tasks as a student's age and grade in school increase.

The *CogAT®* test measures both general and specific reasoning abilities. The general reasoning abilities reflect the overall efficiency of cognitive processes and strategies that enable individuals to learn new tasks and solve problems in the absence of direct instruction. These abilities are assessed in three domains: verbal, quantitative, and nonverbal. Each domain is represented by two or three different reasoning tasks to ensure the dependability of the score that is reported for each student.

CogAT® Practice Test – Levels E and F   Bright Kids NYC Inc ©

CogAT® Content and Format

The Cognitive Abilities Test (*CogAT®*) is designed primarily for use in schools in order to evaluate general cognitive abilities that are fundamental to achieving instructional objectives at each grade. Since the primary purpose of the *CogAT®* is to provide a description of the levels and types of cognitive resources that a student has for learning, separate batteries appraise general cognitive skills using verbal, quantitative, and nonverbal test tasks.

Each battery of the *CogAT®* uses a variety of test tasks such as verbal classification, sentence completion, and verbal analogies. These tasks were selected because research has demonstrated that they are valid measures of abstract reasoning skills and are developmentally appropriate for the age and the grade level of the students being tested. Although the same kinds of abstract reasoning skills are tested from Kindergarten through grade 12, developmental differences between students in the primary grades and those in grades 3 through 12 require that different types of test tasks be used. In addition, the procedures for administrating the *CogAT®* are different for Kindergarten through early grade 3 from those used in grades 3 through 12. To accommodate these developmental differences, *CogAT®* has two separate series' of tests: a Primary Battery containing Levels K through 2, and a Multilevel Battery containing Levels A through H.

CogAT® **Practice Test – Levels E and F**   Bright Kids NYC Inc ©

CogAT® Multilevel Battery Subtest Descriptions

The *CogAT®* Multilevel Battery has eight levels (A-H), and is designed for use in grades 3-12. The Multilevel Battery contains three batteries, each with three subtests and requiring about 45 to 50 minutes to complete.

All *CogAT®* subtests are constructed in a modular format. Easy items are dropped and more difficult items are added as one moves across levels. Each Level, A through H, has three batteries – Verbal, Quantitative, and Nonverbal. There are three subtests on each battery for a total of nine subtests on the *CogAT®*. The time limits are adequate for the majority of students to attempt to answer all of the items. All questions are multiple-choice with five answer choices, except for the first subtest in the Quantitative Battery, which has three answer choices. Students mark their answers on a separate *CogAT®* answer sheet.

Directions for each subtest are printed in the student test booklet. Before students begin a subtest, the test administrator reads the directions aloud while the students read them silently. Students must read or examine each item for themselves and pace themselves to complete all of the items within the allotted time. All of the subtests on the Verbal Battery require reading either single words or sentences; therefore, a student's performance on a subtest in this battery can be influenced by general reading or language skills. The first subtest on the Quantitative Battery also requires some reading. In this subtest, each item presents a pair of quantities or concepts, and students judge whether one quantity is greater than, less than, or equal to the other quantity in the pair. It is unlikely that general reading or language skills affect performance on this subtest to any great degree. Less than one-half of the items at any level of the test have words in each of the items making up the pair, and most of these are either words for coins, money, or measurement. Most of the reading in the subtest is in the three answer choices that are always presented in the same order. The other two subtests on the Quantitative Battery and those on the Nonverbal Battery do not involve reading words.

All of the subtests on each battery appraise general inductive and deductive abstract reasoning skills. The Verbal and Quantitative batteries are designed to appraise more specific verbal and quantitative reasoning skills, in addition to the more general skills. Although the Nonverbal Battery appraises some figural reasoning skills, it is primarily a measure of general inductive reasoning. As the student progresses through school, more specific verbal and quantitative reasoning skills become increasingly important for learning and problem solving in different areas of study. The student's acquired skills and knowledge also become more differentiated and specialized.

Verbal Battery: The three subtests on the Verbal Battery appraise verbal inductive and deductive reasoning skills, as well as flexibility, fluency, and adaptability in working with verbal materials and solving verbal problems. Successful performance on these subtests requires that students have a variety of verbal strategies that they can use effectively. This cluster of verbal reasoning abilities plays an important role in developing skills in reading comprehension, critical thinking, writing, and all other verbal learning tasks.

Quantitative Battery: The three subtests on the Quantitative Battery appraise deductive and inductive reasoning skills as well as flexibility and fluency in working with quantitative symbols and concepts. The Equation Building test also tests the ability to organize, structure, and give meaning to an unordered set of numerals and mathematical symbols. Successful performance on these subtests requires that students have a variety of strategies for working with quantitative materials. The reasoning skills appraised by this battery are significantly related to high-level problem solving not only in mathematics, but also in order disciplines.

Nonverbal Battery: The three subtests on the Nonverbal Battery present the most novel problems to students. The items on these subtests use only geometric shapes and figures that have little direct relationship to formal school instruction. These subtests require no reading and no outside fund of knowledge. Items require reasoning, not spatial visualization abilities, and so there are no gender differences on the battery. To perform successfully, students must have well-developed strategies for dealing with novel materials. Students must be flexible in using these strategies and accurate in implementing them. All three subtests appraise general inductive reasoning skills as well as flexibility and fluency in using and adapting cognitive strategies. The Nonverbal Battery is particularly suitable for obtaining an accurate estimate of cognitive development for students who have difficulty with reading, who have limited proficiency in English, or who have had very limited opportunities to acquire verbal or quantitative knowledge.

Table 1: Structure of the *CogAT®* Multilevel Edition, Levels A-H

Subtests	Number of Items
Verbal Battery	
Verbal Classification	20
Sentence Completion	20
Verbal Analogies	25
Quantitative Battery	
Quantitative Relations	25
Number Series	20
Equation Building	15
Nonverbal Battery	
Figure Classification	25
Figure Analogies	25
Figure Analysis	15
Total	**190**

CogAT® Practice Test – Levels E and F

Scoring Guidelines

When it comes to the results of the *CogAT®* test, they comprise a wealth of useful information for test takers. The scores can be used as follows:

1) To create individualized instruction: Each student gets a score report that includes stanines, relative strengths and weaknesses, and as extreme score differences.

2) To identify gifted students: The high ceiling on the *CogAT®* allows for reliable discrimination among the top 10 percent of scores in all age groups.

3) To predict achievement: The *CogAT®* has been normed with the Iowa Test of Basic Skills® (ITBS®) and the Iowa Tests of Educational Development®. The joint norming of *CogAT®* with elementary and secondary school achievement tests allows for predicting likely achievement levels of students tested with *CogAT®*.

4) To identify at-risk students.

5) To evaluate current and new curricula.

Each child receives a Composite or a Total Score on the *CogAT®* as well as a stanine or a percentile rank. The Composite or Total Score indicates the overall strength of the student's cognitive resources for learning. As the level of the Composite Score decreases, the variety and strength of the student's cognitive resources also decreases and the need for help with learning increases. Students with an above-average or very high Composite Score have an array of strongly developed cognitive resources. They usually learn quickly and typically need no special help to achieve instructional objectives. Students with a below-average or very low Composite Score have very few and weak cognitive resources, typically learn very slowly, and need considerable assistance to achieve instructional objectives.

The Bright Kids *CogAT®* Practice Test can only be scored based on the total number of correct answers, or the overall raw score. Since this practice test has not been standardized with the *CogAT®*, scaled scores, stanines, or percentile ranks cannot be obtained from the raw score. Please realize that a child can miss many questions on the test and still obtain a high score. Thus, it is important that this practice test is utilized as a learning tool to help evaluate a child's strengths and weaknesses rather than to estimate a stanine or a percentile rank.

CogAT® Practice Test – Levels E and F   Bright Kids NYC Inc ©

How to Use this Book

The *CogAT®* Multilevel Battery has eight levels (A-H) and is designed for use in grades 3-12. The test is timed and self-administered, where the student reads and answers questions independently. Instruct the student to write their responses on the answer sheet provided.

We have combined levels E and F to create one practice test because:

(1) Both E and F can be given in grades 6 through 9, depending on the school district and the level of the students in that district.

(2) All *CogAT®* subtests are constructed in a modular format. Easy items are dropped and more difficult items are added as one moves across levels. This means that three to four of the easiest questions are dropped from level E to create level F. The two tests have the same format and exactly the same structure with the exception of a few questions at the end of each subset that are slightly more difficult for children taking the Level E test.

We have also included answer sheets for your child to ensure that he or she practices filling in the bubbles. Please also review the following proven test-taking strategies to help your child succeed on the test:

1. **Listen to all the instructions carefully.** Each section has its own specific instructions for each subtest so it is important for children not to assume but actually understand what is asked of them.

2. **Look at all the answer choices before choosing an answer.** Since no extra credit is given for finishing the test ahead of time, it is important for children to look at all answer choices carefully before selecting a final answer.

3. **Read all the questions thoroughly.** Some children stress for time and start picking answers before reading the question to the end. Many of the questions have information at the end that is critical in solving the problem accurately.

4. **Use process of elimination to get to the right answer.** This is especially important if children are unsure of how exactly to solve the problem, but can intuitively deduct the answer form the answer choices available to them.

5. **Skip questions that seem hard or confusing.** Since each correct answer is given the same credit, it is important not to waste time on questions that are difficult to children. Since the test is timed, wasting time on one question can prevent children from spending time on questions that they can answer correctly.

6. **If all else fails, take a guess.** Many children skip questions, but never have time to return to them. It is important to allocate a little time to make sure that all the questions have a marked answer, since there are no penalties for incorrect answers.

General Administration Guidelines

The test is typically administered in two or three different settings. There is a short rest period recommended if two subtests are administered in one sitting.

The recommended timeline is as follows:

First Sitting - Verbal Battery

Distributing Materials & Practice Questions	*Approximately 5 minutes*
Test 1: Oral Classification	Approximately 13 minutes
Test 2: Sentence Completion	Approximately 13 minutes
Test 3: Verbal Analogies	Approximately 13 minutes

Second Sitting - Quantitative Battery

Distributing Materials & Practice Questions	*Approximately 5 minutes*
Test 4: Quantitative relations	Approximately 12 minutes
Test 5: Number Series	Approximately 13 minutes
Test 6: Equation Building	Approximately 15 minutes

Third Sitting - Nonverbal Battery

Distributing Materials & Practice Questions	*Approximately 5 minutes*
Test 7: Figure Classification	Approximately 13 minutes
Test 8: Figure Analogies	Approximately 13 minutes
Test 9: Figure Analysis	Approximately 13 minutes

Getting Ready

Materials

1. Answer Sheets removed from the end of the book.

2. Several No. 2 soft lead pencils, erasers, and pencil sharpeners.

3. Ideally, a "Do Not Disturb" sign for the room where you will be administering the test.

Prior to Testing

1. Familiarize yourself with the test and the instructions. Take the actual test to make sure that you can later explain to the child why certain answers are correct or incorrect.

2. Provide satisfactory physical conditions in the room where the child will be taking the test. Make sure that there is ample lighting and ventilation.

3. To prevent interruptions, give the child the test when there are no other distractions in the house. If the house is not suitable, try to find a local library or a school.

During Testing

1. Make sure that the child knows how to accurately mark the answers. Help the child as needed by utilizing the sample questions.

2. Make sure the child understands the test directions and utilize the sample questions to answer the questions before you begin each section of the test.

3. Pace the test and utilize the breaks as needed, but adhere to the time limits of each test. Do not attempt to complete the test in one sitting.

4. Do not give the child any feedback during testing. Discuss the answers only after the testing is complete.

5. Always provide positive reinforcements to ensure that the child completes the task.

CogAT® Practice Test – Levels E and F Bright Kids NYC Inc ©

Bright Kids NYC
CogAT® Practice Test

Multilevel Battery

Levels E and F

CogAT® Practice Test – Levels E and F   Bright Kids NYC Inc ©

TEST 1: VERBAL CLASSIFICATION

The questions on this test are just like the sample below.

SAMPLE

Triangle   **Rectangle**   **Circle**   **?**

A. Shape   B. Table   C. Square   D. Round   E. Draw

The first three words are triangle, rectangle and circle, which are all shapes. Thus, we are looking for an answer that is a shape. The correct answer is C, a square, which is also a shape. Find the place marked, **Test 1: Verbal Classification** on your answer sheet. Look for the item that is marked as S, which is the sample question. Since the answer is C, fill in the answer space C in the row marked as S.

Answer all of the questions on this test the same way. Try your best to answer each question.

CogAT® Practice Test – Levels E and F   Bright Kids NYC Inc ©

1. Run   Stroll   Walk   ?

A. Jog   B. Sit   C. Swim   D. Awake   E. Sleep

2. Engine   Nose   Wings   ?

A. Fly   B. Tail   C. Pilot   D. Bumper   E. Plane

3. Semicolon   Comma   Hyphen   ?

A. Apostrophe   B. Sentence   C. Paragraph   D. Adjective   E. Punctuation

4. Cardiologist   Veterinarian   Pediatrician   ?

A. Nurse   B. Doctor   C. Medicine   D. Hospital   E. Anesthesiologist

5. North America   Antarctica   Africa   ?

A. Australia   B. Country   C. Continent   D. United States   E. Hawaii

6. Dill   Oregano   Cilantro   ?

A. Herbs   B. Spicy   C. Mustard   D. Condiment   E. Basil

7. Honey   Glue   Tape   ?

A. Bee   B. Paper   C. Water   D. Gum   E. Crayon

8. Mimic   Copy   Repeat   ?

A. Alter   B. Change   C. Irritate   D. Misrepresent   E. Imitate

9. Urge   **Insist**   **Order** ?

A. Abandon   B. Perceive   C. Demand   D. Concede   E. React

10. Arrogant   **Pompous**   **Boastful**   ?

A. Timid   B. Modest   C. Polite   D. Courteous   E. Lofty

11. Disperse   **Scatter**   **Distribute**   ?

A. Discard   B. Include   C. Collect   D. Dissipate   E. Gather

12. Humor   **Temper**   **Mood**   ?

A. Mind   B. Disposition   C. Personality   D. Character   E. Drive

13. Chapter   **Glossary**   **Index**   ?

A. Foreword   B. Fiction   C. Paragraph   D. Pages   E. Author

14. Trunk   **Branch**   **Leaf**   ?

A. Root   B. Tree   C. Forest   D. Pollen   E. Dirt

15. Lava   **Ashes**   **Pumice**   ?

A. Erupt   B. Gas   C. Volcano   D. Mountain   E. Hot

16. Primary   **Principal**   **Original**   ?

A. Ordinary   B. Pastel   C. Chief   D. Inferior   E. Subsequent

17. Stirrup   **Hoof**   **Bridle**   **?**

A. Antler   B. Animal   C. Jockey   D. Horse   E. Saddle

18. Defendant   **Juror**   **Prosecutor**   **?**

A. Courtroom   B. Witness   C. Law   D. Testimony   E. Evidence

19. Almond   **Cashew**   **Peanut**   **?**

A. Pinecone   B. Tree   C. Pecan   D. Nut   E. Food

20. Shore   **Coast**   **Beach**   **?**

A. Island   B. Bay   C. Strand   D. River   E. Pond

CogAT® **Practice Test – Levels E and F**   Bright Kids NYC Inc ©

TEST 2: SENTENCE COMPLETION

The questions on this test are just like the sample below.

SAMPLE:

The sign stopped people from entering the room, since it could be _____ .

A. Clean   B. Wrong   C. Dangerous   D. Safe   E. Dull

Read the sentence and each of the answers below it. Find the word that makes the most sense to help complete the sentence. The correct answer is: C, Dangerous. Find the place marked, **Test 2: Sentence Completion** on your answer sheet. Look for the item that is marked as S, which is the sample question. Since the answer is C, fill in the answer space C in the row marked as S.

Answer all of the questions on this test the same way. Try your best to answer each question.

CogAT® Practice Test – Levels E and F

1. Once the picture is dry, you won't be able to _____ the colors.

A. Paint   B. Color   C. Touch   D. See   E. Alter

2. Not all animals are mammals, _____ all mammals are animals.

A. So   B. Therefore   C. And   D. If   E. But

3. The coach _____ the team on their hard work and perseverance.

A. Dismissed   B. Scolded   C. Complimented   D. Ignored   E. Helped

4. Cathy stored the remaining food in vacuum-sealed bags, to _____ the food from going stale.

A. Maintain   B. Remove   C. Create   D. Prevent   E. Help

5. Since Kate could hear the _____, she knew that the police were on their way.

A. Loud   B. Siren   C. Yelling   D. Lights   E. Mirror

6. Francis was so _____ from the race that she took a nap before going out.

A. Frantic   B. Exhausted   C. Dehydrated   D. Excited   E. Worried

7. The typhoon just missed the most crowded seaside city in the country; the rising sea caused by the storm could have been _____.

A. Catastrophic   B. Fantastic   C. Unlikely   D. Visible   E. Amusing

8. John was so _____ that no matter how much he drank, he could not quench his thirst.

A. Hungry   B. Exhausted   C. Tired   D. Dehydrated   E. Annoyed

9. It was was so foggy that you could hardly see the _____ skyscrapers.

    A. Far   B. Ahead   C. Immense   D. Endless   E. Small

10. She _____ expected her parents to pay for her trip, even though she spent all her money on a new computer.

    A. Perhaps   B. Maybe   C. Still   D. Almost   E. Also

11. I _____ wanted to go to the party, but I was too tired from working all day.

    A. Really   B. Maybe   C. Perhaps   D. Never   E. Totally

12. Pompeei was destroyed by an enormous _____ covering the city with volcanic ash and lava.

    A. Eruption   B. Explosion   C. Expansion   D. Growth   E. Prosperity

13. As the sun set, the trees started _____ long shadows, finally creating some much needed shade.

    A. Casting   B. Making   C. Distributing   D. Growing   E. Missing

14. Some people say advice stems from recalling one's previous _____.

    A. Events   B. Hopes   C. Mistakes   D. Ambitions   E. Aspirations

15. It is easy to give up if you don't succeed; but those who succeed always _____.

    A. Give Up   B. Persevere   C. Hope   D. Assert   E. Win

16. She was _____ when she found out her poem won first prize, as she didn't spend much time writing it.

    A. Happy   B. Shocked   C. Elated   D. Upset   E. Mad

17. He never once gave up after his injury, and didn't allow himself to _____.

    A. Quit   B. Win   C. Succeed   D. Work   E. Complain

18. Those who don't _____ carefully often forget things.

    A. Laugh   B. Eat   C. Play   D. Listen   E. Walk

19. The sports club _____ a discounted membership fee for all its old members.

    A. Reinstated   B. Eliminated   C. Offered   D. Fulfilled   E. Waived

20. Sometimes extraordinary events happen; for example, a rainbow can appear in the sky _____ it is still raining.

    A. Since   B. Maybe   C. While   D. If   E. Unless

CogAT® **Practice Test – Levels E and F**   Bright Kids NYC Inc ©

TEST 3: VERBAL ANALOGIES

The questions on this test are just like the sample below.

SAMPLE:

In is to Out   as   **Left is to ?**

A. Right   B. Side   C. In   D. Direction   E. Between

The first two words are in and out. These words are related in a certain way. In is the opposite of out. Look at the third word. The answer we are looking for must have the same relationship with "Left" as the first two words, in and out, have with each other. Hence, we are looking for the opposite of left, which is right. The correct answer is A. Find the place marked **Test 3: Verbal Analogies** on your answer sheet. Look for the item that is marked as S, which is the sample question. Since the answer is A, fill in the answer space A in the row marked as S.

Answer all of the questions on this test the same way. Try your best to answer each question.

1. Yard is to Inch   as   Quart is to ?

A. Gallon   B. Liter   C. Cup   D. Milk   E. Measure

2. Tease is to Cry   as   Joke is to ?

A. Cry   B. Laugh   C. Clown   D. Comedian   E. Play

3. Exercise is to Gym   as   Graze is to ?

A. Cow   B. Eat   C. Pasture   D. Hay   E. Nibble

4. Propeller is to Airplane   as   Wick is to ?

A. Burn   B. Candle   C. Wicker   D. Flame   E. Light

5. Person is to Talk   as   Bird is to ?

A. Birdhouse   B. Chirp   C. Cry   D. Eat   E. Hunt

6. Cell is to Microscope   as   Star is to ?

A. Comet   B. Sun   C. Constellation   D. Telescope   E. Gaze

7. Wolf is to Pack   as   Person is to ?

A. Concert   B. Play   C. Human   D. Men   E. Family

8. Banana is to Peel   as   Corn is to ?

A. Cob   B. Husk   C. Kernel   D. Vegetable   E. Eat

9. Fish is to Water   as   **Crocodile is to ?**

A. Reptile   B. Cage   C. Land   D. Zoo   E. Fly

10. Ruby is to Gem   as   **Shirt is to ?**

A. Clothes   B. Pair   C. Laundry   D. Wear   E. Hands

11. Run is to Jog   as   **Rain is to ?**

A. Pour   B. Hurricane   C. Umbrella   D. Wet   E. Drizzle

12. Referee is to Basketball   as   **Umpire is to ?**

A. Sports   B. Baseball   C. Team   D. Football   E. Catcher

13. Fin is to Fish   as   **Rudder is to ?**

A. Oar   B. Sail   C. Schooner   D. Boat   E. Mast

14. Scold is to Reprimand   as   **Persevere is to ?**

A. Coast   B. Disregard   C. Linger   D. Persist   E. Determine

15. Saw is to Carpenter   as   **Microscope is to ?**

A. Telescope   B. Scientist   C. Measure   D. Look   E. Lens

16. Radish is to Vegetable   as   **Specific is to ?**

A. Characteristic   B. General   C. Eat   D. Part   E. Special

17. Mare is to Stallion   **as**   **Doe is to ?**

A. Buck   B. Horse   C. Deer   D. Fawn   E. Calf

18. Clock is to Hand   **as**   **Wheel is to ?**

A. Wheelbarrow   B. Road   C. Spoke   D. Car   E. Tire

19. Ingredients is to Recipe   **as**   **Picture is to ?**

A. Paint   B. Write   C. Collage   D. Pen   E. Tree

20. Temperature is to Thermometer   **as**   **Wind is to ?**

A. Weathervane   B. Anemometer   C. Blow   D. Hurricane   E. Air

21. Orchestra is to Musician   **as**   **Many is to ?**

A. One   B. Few   C. More   D. Any   E. None

22. Bind is to Knit   **as**   **Book is to ?**

A. Needles   B. Sweater   C. Library   D. Page   E. Fiction

23. Embarrassed is to Humiliated   **as**   **Frightened is to ?**

A. Annoyed   B. Agitated   C. Terrified   D. Courageous   E. Fearless

24. Sponge is to Porous   **as**   **Rubber is to ?**

A. Elastic   B. Inflexible   C. Tire   D. Massive   E. Solid

25. Anywher is to Somewhere   as   Country is to ?

A. Live   B. Earth   C. England   D. President   E. Continent

TEST 4: QUANTITATIVE RELATIONS

The questions on this test are just like the sample below. In each question, there are two mathematical concepts to compare. The objective is to decide which one is bigger or if both are equal. Please utilize scratch paper as needed.

SAMPLE:

> **I. $5 + 0$**
> **II. $0 + 5$**

A. I is greater than II
B. I is less than II
C. I is equal to II

Look at the equations I and II at the top. Calculate the value of I and II. Then, look at the answer choices below to see if I is greater than II, less than II, or equal to II. Since I and II are equal to 5, the correct answer is C, I is equal to II. Find the place marked **Test 4: Quantitative Relations** on your answer sheet. Look for the item that is marked as S, which is the sample question. Since the answer is C, fill in the answer space C in the row marked as S.

Answer all of the questions on this test the same way. Try your best to answer each question.

CogAT® Practice Test – Levels E and F Bright Kids NYC Inc ©

1.   I. 80 – 40
        II. 80 ÷ 2

A. I is greater than II
B. I is less than II
C. I is equal to II

2.   I. 180 seconds
        II. 2 minutes

A. I is a longer time than II
B. I is a shorter time than II
C. I is the same length of time as II

3.   I. The distance across a rectangle
        II. The distance around the same rectangle

A. I is greater than II
B. I is less than II
C. I is equal to II

4.   I. 2 Liters
        II. ½ Gallon

A. I is more than II
B. I is less than II
C. I is the same amount as II

5.   I. 0.2
        II. $\dfrac{1}{5}$

A. I is greater than II
B. I is less than II
C. I is equal to II

6.   **I. The Sides of a Hexagon**
      II. The Sides of an Octagon

A. I is more than II
B. I is less than II
C. I is the same as II

7.   **I. The number of dimes to make 50 cents**
      II. The number of pennies to make a nickel

A. I is greater than II
B. I is less than II
C. I is equal to II

8.   **I. 64**
      II. 4 x 4 x 4

A. I is greater than II
B. I is less than II
C. I is equal to II

9.   **I.** $\dfrac{2}{4}$
      II. $\dfrac{4}{8}$

A. I is greater than II
B. I is less than II
C. I is equal to II

10.   **I. 19+14-6**
      II. 20+9-2

A. I is greater than II
B. I is less than II
C. I is equal to II

11.   **I. 0.3**
      II. 0.030

A. I is greater than II
B. I is less than II
C. I is equal to II

12.   **I. 0.20**
      II. $\dfrac{1}{8}$

A. I is greater than II
B. I is less than II
C. I is equal to II

13.   **I.** $\dfrac{4}{3}$
      II. $\dfrac{3}{4}$

A. I is greater than II
B. I is less than II
C. I is equal to II

14.   **I. 17+3-6+3**
      II. 16-6+4+2

A. I is greater than II
B. I is less than II
C. I is equal to II

15.   **I.** $\dfrac{(62-8)}{9}$
      II. $\dfrac{(48+6)}{6}$

A. I is greater than II
B. I is less than II
C. I is equal to II

16.   **Given:**
        A is greater than B, and
        C is less than B

A. A is greater than C
B. A is less than C
C. A is equal to C

17.   **I. 9^2**
        II. $3^2 + 3^3$

A. I is greater than II
B. I is less than II
C. I is equal to II

18.   **Given:**
        X-3=4 and
        Y+1=7

A. X^2 is greater than Y^2
B. X^2 is less than Y^2
C. X^2 is equal to Y^2

19.   **Given:**
        X-5=0 and
        Y-6=-1

A. X is greater than Y
B. X is less than Y
C. X is equal to Y

20.   **Given:**
        X=Z-4 and
        Y=Z+4

A. X is greater than Y
B. X is less than Y
C. X is equal to Y

21. Given:
A is less than B, and
A+B = B+C

A. A is more than C
B. A is less than C
C. A is equal to C

22. Given:
$$\frac{X}{4} = 2, \text{ and}$$
$$\frac{Y}{2} = 4$$

A. X is more than Y
B. X is less than Y
C. X is equal to Y

23. I. $\frac{1}{8}$ x $\frac{1}{8}$
   II. $\frac{1}{4}$ x $\frac{1}{4}$ x $\frac{1}{4}$

A. I is more than II
B. I is less than II
C. I is equal to II

24. Given:
F + 1 is less than E, and
F is greater than 0

A. E^2 is more than F^2
B. E^2 is less than F^2
C. E^2 is equal to F^2

25.   **Given:**
             D= A+B, and
             E= A-B, and
             B is less than 0

A. D is greater than E
B. D is less than E
C. D is equal to E

TEST 5: NUMBER SERIES

The questions on this test are just like the sample below. Each question has a series of numbers. Find out the rule associated with each series, and then by applying the same rule, find out what must come next.

SAMPLE:

1	2	3	4	5	?

A. 6   B. 7   C. 8   D. 9   E. 5

Look at the number series above and find out the rule associated with the series. Each number is one more than the number before it. One plus one is two; two plus one is three; three plus one is four; four plus one is five. Applying the same rule, the next number should be one more than the last one. Since five plus one is six, the correct answer is A, six. Find the place marked **Test 5: Number Series** on your answer sheet. Look for the item that is marked as S, which is the sample question. Since the answer is A, fill in the answer space A in the row marked as S.

Answer all of the questions on this test the same way. Try your best to answer each question.

CogAT® Practice Test – Levels E and F   Bright Kids NYC Inc ©

1.   5   6   **10**   **11**   **15**   **16**   **?**

A. 17   B. 20   C. 21   D. 18   E. 12

2.   6   3   **6**   **4**   **6**   **?**

A. 0   B. 5   C. 3   D. 1   E. 4

3.   1   0   **3**   **2**   **5**   **?**

A. 0   B. 5   C. 3   D. 6   E. 4

4.   4   9   **14**   **14**   **9**   **?**

A. 5   B. 2   C. 4   D. 6   E. 7

5.   13   18   **14**   **17**   **15**   **?**

A. 14   B. 18   C. 17   D. 16   E. 13

6.   2   8   **13**   **17**   **20**   **?**

A. 21   B. 22   C. 17   D. 20   E. 19

7.   5   7   **10**   **4**   **6**   **9**   **?**

A. 4   B. 5   C. 3   D. 10   E. 8

8.   11   14   **12**   **15**   **13**   **16**   **?**

A. 19   B. 14   C. 13   D. 17   E. 18

9.   **3**   **4**   **7**   **12**   **19**   **?**

A. 29   B. 30   C. 34   D. 28   E. 24

10.   **8**   **13**   **15**   **16**   **15**   **13 ?**

A. 12   B. 8   C. 16   D. 14   E. 10

11.   **32**   **16**   **48**   **24**   **72**   **?**

A. 36   B. 54   C. 64   D. 48   E. 32

12.   **1**   **4**   **2**   **6**   **3**   **?**

A. 4   B. 5   C. 8   D. 7   E. 9

13.   **7**   **8**   **10**   **13**   **17**   **?**

A. 20   B. 15   C. 23   D. 22   E. 25

14.   **1** $1\frac{1}{4}$ $1\frac{1}{2}$ $1\frac{3}{4}$ **?**

A. $2\frac{1}{4}$ B. $1\frac{4}{3}$ C. $1\frac{5}{8}$ D. $1\frac{2}{4}$ E. 2

15.   **15**   **17**   **21**   **27**   **?**

A. 33   B. 21   C. 35   D. 37   E. 19

16.   **2**   **7**   **13**   **3**   **8**   **14**   **?**

A. 4   B. 19   C. 18   D. 11   E. 12

17.   8   4   12   10   5   15   12   ?

A. 8   B. 6   C. 30   D. 24   E. 12

18.   5   3   6   10   5   11   18   ?

A. 8   B. 10   C. 26   D. 11   E. 12

19.   45   33   23   15   ?

A. 7   B. 11   C. 9   D. 10   E. 12

20.   12   5   17   7   24   9   ?

A. 31   B. 35   C. 33   D. 7   E. 12

CogAT® **Practice Test – Levels E and F**   Bright Kids NYC Inc ©

TEST 6: EQUATION BUILDING

The questions on this test are just like the sample below. For each equation there are some numbers and signs. You must combine all the numbers and signs until you can make an equation that equals one of the answer choices.

SAMPLE:

1   3   5   +   -

A. 4   B. 8   C. 9   D. 4   E. 7

The question above has three numbers, a plus sign and a minus sign. You can combine these numbers in different ways:

$5 + 1 - 3 = 3$
$5 + 3 - 2 = 6$
$5 - 3 + 1 = 7$

While all the answers above are correct, there is only one, 7, which is listed in the answer choices. Therefore, the correct answer is E, 7. Find the place marked **Test 6: Equation Building** on your answer sheet. Look for the item that is marked as S, which is the sample question. Since the answer is E, fill in the answer space E in the row marked as S.

Answer all of the questions on this test the same way. Try your best to answer each question.

CogAT® Practice Test – Levels E and F   Bright Kids NYC Inc ©

1.   **4**   **4**   **4**   **x**   **x**

A. 16   B. 8   C. 64   D. 36   E. 18

2.   **3**   **4**   **7**   **+**   **-**

A. 14   B. 9   C. 6   D. 7   E. 1

3.   **2**   **4**   **10**   **+**   **÷**

A. 6   B. 16   C. 8   D. 14   E. 9

4.   **1**   **3**   **5**   **x**   **+**

A. 15   B. 17   C. 16   D. 9   E. 2

5.   **2**   **4**   **4**   **8**   **x**   **÷**   **÷**

A. 5   B. 4   C. 3   D. 40   E. 18

6.   **1**   **4**   **5**   **7**   **+**   **+**   **-**

A. 4   B. 9   C. 17   D. 8   E. 10

7. $\frac{1}{5}$ $\frac{1}{5}$ $\frac{1}{5}$ **x**   **÷**

A. $\frac{1}{5}$ B. $\frac{1}{25}$ C. $\frac{1}{125}$ D. $\frac{2}{5}$ E. $\frac{1}{10}$

8.   **2**   **5**   **8**   **9**   **+**   **+**   **-**

A. 21   B. 24   C. 6   D. 9   E. 10

9. **2** **4** **6** **12** x ÷ ÷

A. 24   B. 9   C. 6   D. 10   E. 18

10. **4** **10** **14** ÷ + ( )

A. 8   B. 1   C. 9   D. 10   E. 11

11. **2** **5** **6** **10** + + -

A. 19   B. 23   C. 9   D. 10   E. 14

12. **6** **9** **12** - x ( )

A. 27   B. 48   C. 17   D. 18   E. 24

13. **6** **9** **12** x ÷

A. 27   B. 48   C. 17   D. 18   E. 24

14. **1** **6** **18** x ÷

A. 1   B. 4   C. 1/2   D. 1/3   E. 6

15. $\dfrac{1}{4}$ **4** **16** x - ( )

A. 10   B. 0   C. 4   D. 1/2   E. 32

TEST 7: FIGURE CLASSIFICATION

The questions on this test are just like the sample below. The first three figures are alike in each question. The objective is to find their common characteristic and decide what other figure from the answer choices belong with the first three.

SAMPLE:

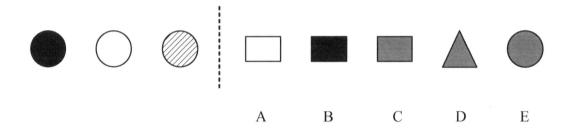

Look at the first three figures and decide what is common among them. Each figure is a circle with different shadings. Hence, we are looking for another circle. The last answer choice is the correct one, a gray circle. Therefore, the correct answer is E. Find the place marked **Test 7: Figure Classification** on your answer sheet. Look for the item that is marked as S, which is the sample question. Since the answer is E, fill in the answer space E in the row marked as S.

Answer all of the questions on this test the same way. Try your best to answer each question.

CogAT® Practice Test – Levels E and F Bright Kids NYC Inc ©

01

      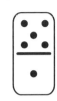 

A B C D E

02

    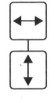

A B C D E

03

A B C D E

04

A B C D E

05

A B C D E

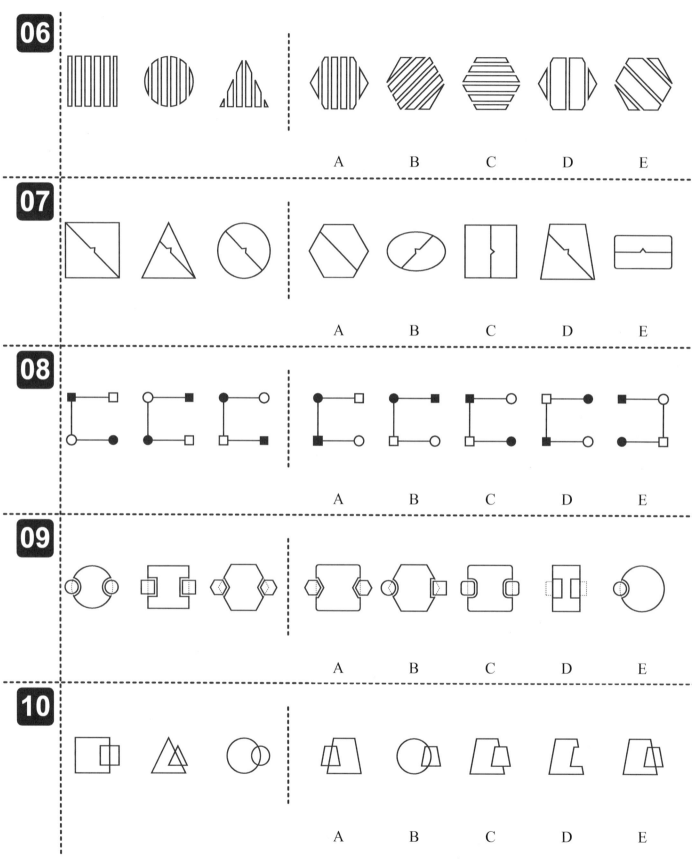

CogAT® Practice Test – Levels E and F   Bright Kids NYC Inc ©

11

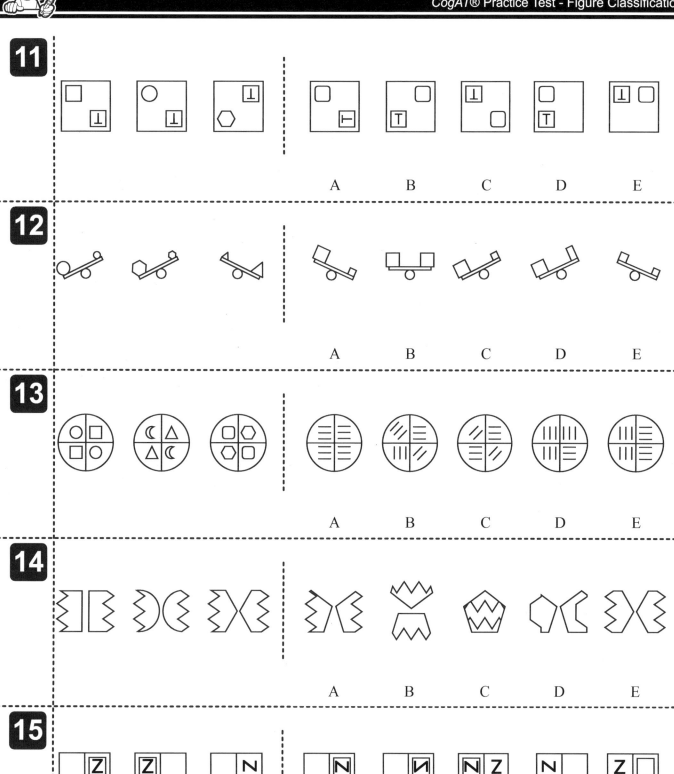

A   B   C   D   E

12

A   B   C   D   E

13

A   B   C   D   E

14

A   B   C   D   E

15

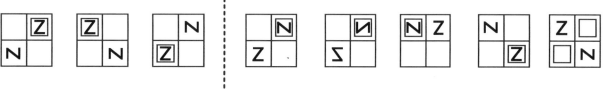

A   B   C   D   E

16

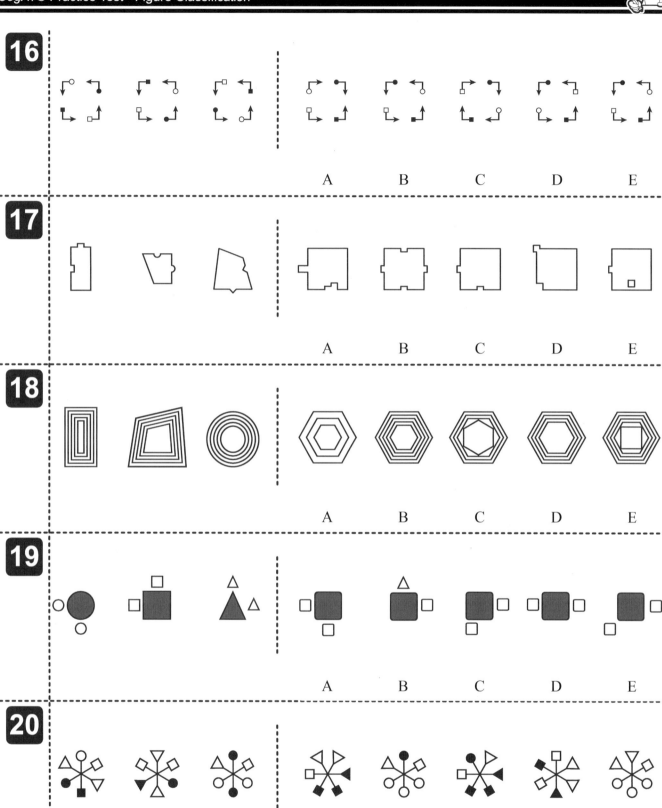

A   B   C   D   E

17

A   B   C   D   E

18

A   B   C   D   E

19

A   B   C   D   E

20

A   B   C   D   E

21

A B C D E

22

A B C D E

23

A B C D E

24

A B C D E

25

A B C D E

CogAT® **Practice Test – Levels E and F**   Bright Kids NYC Inc ©

TEST 8: FIGURE ANALOGIES

The questions on this test are just like the sample below.

SAMPLE:

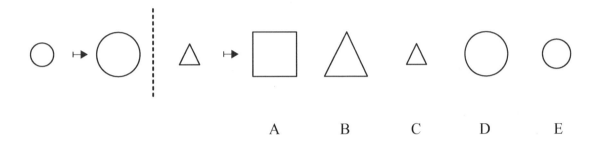

Look at the first two figures. The first is a small circle. The second figure is a large circle. The circle increases in size. The next figure is a small triangle. The small circle goes together with a large circle in the same way the small triangle goes with the large triangle. Thus, the correct answer is B. Find the place marked **Test 8: Figure Analogies** on your answer sheet. Look for the item that is marked as S, which is the sample question. Since the answer is B, fill in the answer space B in the row marked as S.

Answer all of the questions on this test the same way. Try your best to answer each question.

CogAT® Practice Test – Levels E and F

01

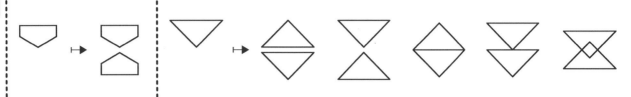

A   B   C   D   E

02

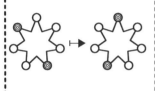 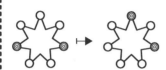

A   B   C   D   E

03

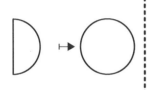 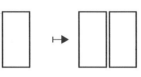

A   B   C   D   E

04

A   B   C   D   E

05

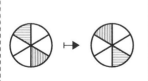 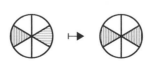

A   B   C   D   E

06

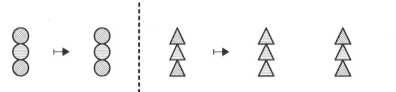

             A   B   C   D   E

07

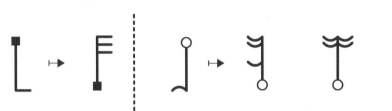

             A   B   C   D   E

08

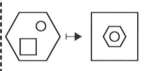

             A   B   C   D   E

09

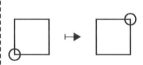

             A   B   C   D   E

10

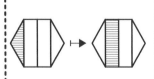

             A   B   C   D   E

11

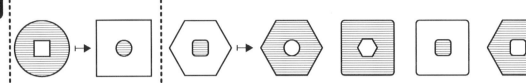

A   B   C   D   E

12

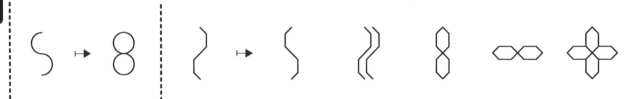

A   B   C   D   E

13

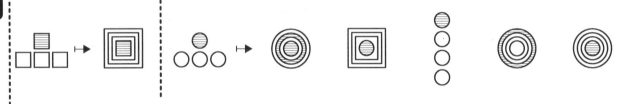

A   B   C   D   E

14

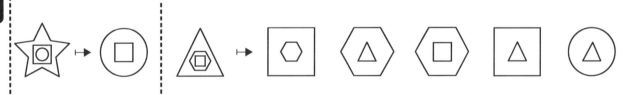

A   B   C   D   E

15

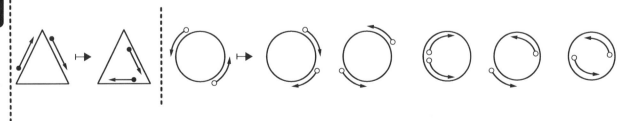

A   B   C   D   E

16

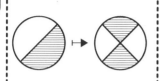

      A   B   C   D   E

17

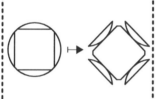   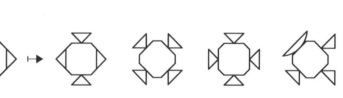

      A   B   C   D   E

18

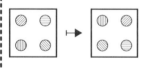

      A   B   C   D   E

19

 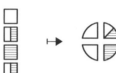

      A   B   C   D   E

20

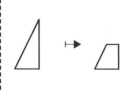

      A   B   C   D   E

21

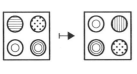 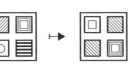

A	B	C	D	E

22

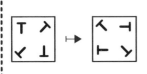 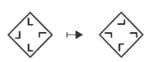

A	B	C	D	E

23

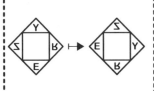 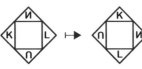

A	B	C	D	E

24

A	B	C	D	E

25

A	B	C	D	E

CogAT® Practice Test – Levels E and F

TEST 9: FIGURE ANALYSIS

The questions on this test are just like the sample below. Each question has a piece of paper that is folded and where holes are punched into it. The objective is to find out how the paper will look when it is unfolded.

SAMPLE:

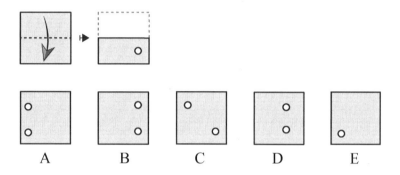

Look at the first square. It shows the way the paper looks before it was folded. The marks show where the middle of each side is, and the dotted line shows where the paper will be folded. The arrow shows the direction of the fold. In this example above, the paper will be folded in half with the top over the bottom.

Next, look at the second square. The shaded area shows the paper after the folding is complete. The dotted lines show the paper size, prior to folding. The white circle shows where the paper has been punched.

Finally, look at the answer choices below. The objective is to find what the paper will now look like when it is unfolded. Please note that the paper has been punched through the folded paper, through two layers. Thus, there must be two holes in the paper, when it is unfolded. Since the paper was folded straight down, the holes must be on top of one another. The hole was punched near the right edge, so the punched wholes must be on the right side. Find the place marked **Test 9: Figure Analysis** on your answer sheet. Look for the item that is marked as S, which is the sample question. Since the answer is B, fill in the answer space B in the row marked as S.

Answer all of the questions on this test the same way. Try your best to answer each question.

CogAT® Practice Test – Levels E and F   Bright Kids NYC Inc ©

01

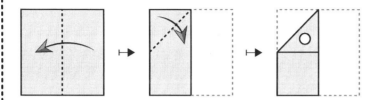

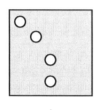   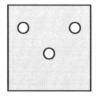   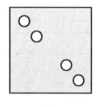   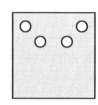

A   B   C   D   E

02

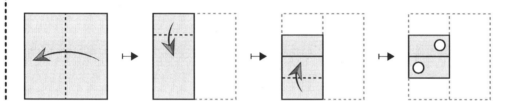

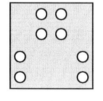   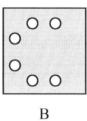   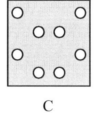   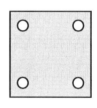   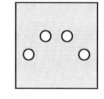

A   B   C   D   E

03

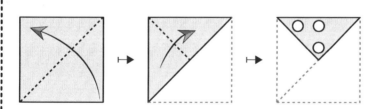

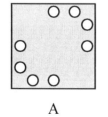   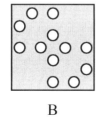   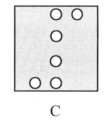   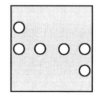   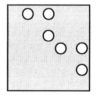

A   B   C   D   E

04

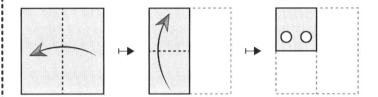

 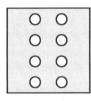  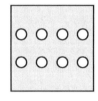 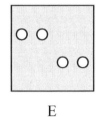

A   B   C   D   E

05

 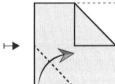 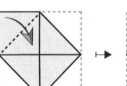

  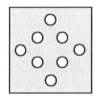 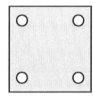

A   B   C   D   E

06

 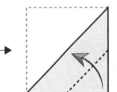

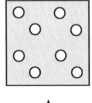   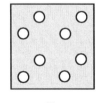 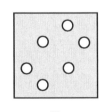

A   B   C   D   E

07

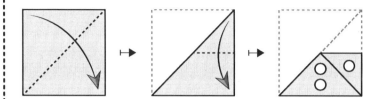

 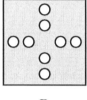 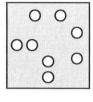 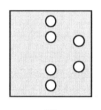 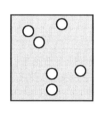

A B C D E

08

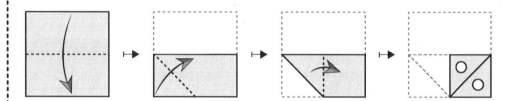

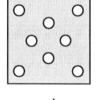 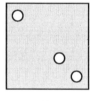 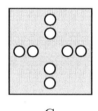 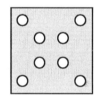 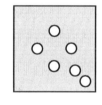

A B C D E

09

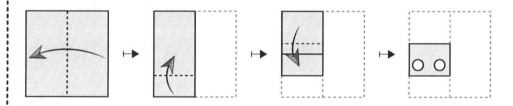

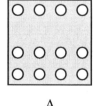 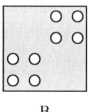 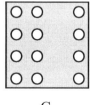 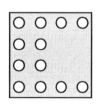 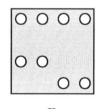

A B C D E

10

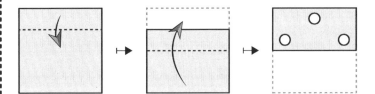

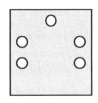 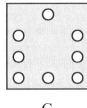 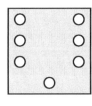 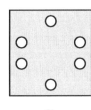

A   B   C   D   E

11

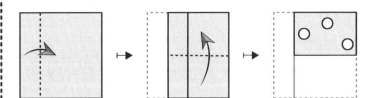

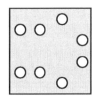 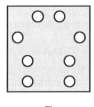 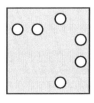 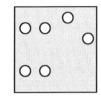

A   B   C   D   E

12

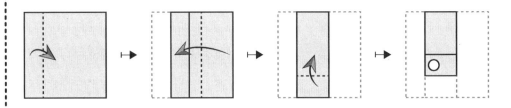

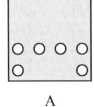 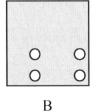 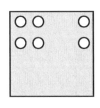 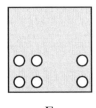

A   B   C   D   E

13

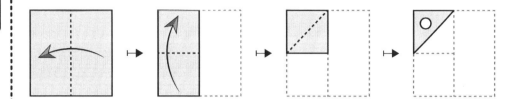

 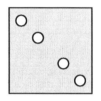 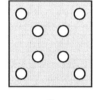 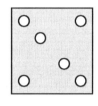 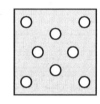

| A | B | C | D | E |

14

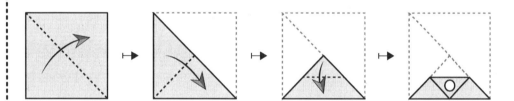

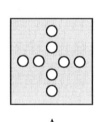 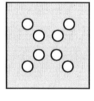 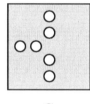 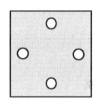 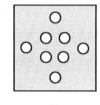

| A | B | C | D | E |

15

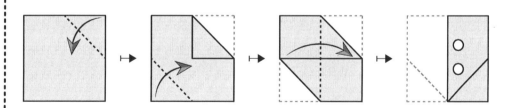

 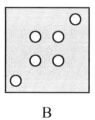   

| A | B | C | D | E |

CogAT® Practice Test – Levels E and F   Bright Kids NYC Inc ©

Answer Keys

CogAT® Practice Test – Levels E and F   Bright Kids NYC Inc ©

Answer Keys

Battery 1: Verbal Battery

	Verbal Classification	Sentence Completion	Verbal Analogies
1.	A	E	C
2.	B	E	B
3.	A	C	C
4.	E	D	B
5.	A	B	B
6.	E	B	C
7.	D	A	E
8.	E	D	B
9.	C	C	C
10.	E	C	A
11.	D	A	E
12.	B	A	B
13.	A	A	D
14.	A	C	D
15.	B	B	B
16.	C	B	B
17.	E	A	A
18.	B	D	C
19.	C	C	C
20.	B	C	B
21.			A
22.			B
23.			C
24.			A
25.			C

Answer Keys

Battery 2: Quantitative Battery

	Quantitative Relations	Number Series	Equation Building
1.	C	B	C
2.	A	B	C
3.	B	E	E
4.	A	C	C
5.	C	D	B
6.	B	B	B
7.	C	C	A
8.	C	B	C
9.	C	D	B
10.	C	B	B
11.	A	A	A
12.	A	C	D
13.	A	D	D
14.	A	E	D
15.	B	C	B
16.	A	A	
17.	A	B	
18.	A	B	
19.	C	C	
20.	B	C	
21.	C		
22.	C		
23.	C		
24.	A		
25.	B		

Answer Keys

Battery 3: Nonverbal Battery

	Figure Classification	Figure Analogies	Figure Analysis
1.	E	B	E
2.	E	E	A
3.	D	D	B
4.	B	E	D
5.	C	C	B
6.	A	C	A
7.	D	D	C
8.	D	C	D
9.	C	A	A
10.	E	D	D
11.	C	B	B
12.	C	C	E
13.	C	E	C
14.	A	A	A
15.	D	E	B
16.	D	A	
17.	C	E	
18.	B	B	
19.	A	E	
20.	D	A	
21.	D	C	
22.	D	C	
23.	E	A	
24.	E	E	
25.	B	A	

Answer Sheets

CogAT® **Practice Test – Answer Sheets**

Bright Kids NYC Inc ©

EXAMPLE

1 (A) (✗) (C) (D) WRONG

2 (✓) (B) (C) (D) WRONG

3 (A) (B) (◠) (D) WRONG

4 (A) (B) (C) (●) CORRECT

DIRECTIONS:

- Use a #2 black lead pencil only.
- Do not use ink or colored pencil.
- Completely fill in one oval per question.
- Erase clearly any answer you wish to change.
- Make no stray marks on this answer sheet.

LAST NAME | FIRST NAME

(Bubble grid with letters A through Z in columns for Last Name and First Name)

DATE OF BIRTH

Month	Year
○ JAN	
○ FEB	(0)(0)
○ MAR	(1)(1)
○ APR	(2)(2)
○ MAY	(3)(3)
○ JUN	(4)(4)
○ JUL	(5)(5)
○ AUG	(6)(6)
○ SEP	(7)(7)
○ OCT	(8)(8)
○ NOV	(9)(9)
○ DEC	

GENDER

○ FEMALE

○ MALE

COGAT LEVEL

S

A

M

P

L

E

CogAT® Practice Test – Answer Sheets   Bright Kids NYC Inc ©

TEST 1: VERBAL CLASSIFICATIONS

S. Ⓐ Ⓑ Ⓒ Ⓓ Ⓔ
1. Ⓐ Ⓑ Ⓒ Ⓓ Ⓔ
2. Ⓐ Ⓑ Ⓒ Ⓓ Ⓔ
3. Ⓐ Ⓑ Ⓒ Ⓓ Ⓔ
4. Ⓐ Ⓑ Ⓒ Ⓓ Ⓔ
5. Ⓐ Ⓑ Ⓒ Ⓓ Ⓔ
6. Ⓐ Ⓑ Ⓒ Ⓓ Ⓔ
7. Ⓐ Ⓑ Ⓒ Ⓓ Ⓔ
8. Ⓐ Ⓑ Ⓒ Ⓓ Ⓔ
9. Ⓐ Ⓑ Ⓒ Ⓓ Ⓔ
10. Ⓐ Ⓑ Ⓒ Ⓓ Ⓔ
11. Ⓐ Ⓑ Ⓒ Ⓓ Ⓔ
12. Ⓐ Ⓑ Ⓒ Ⓓ Ⓔ
13. Ⓐ Ⓑ Ⓒ Ⓓ Ⓔ
14. Ⓐ Ⓑ Ⓒ Ⓓ Ⓔ
15. Ⓐ Ⓑ Ⓒ Ⓓ Ⓔ
16. Ⓐ Ⓑ Ⓒ Ⓓ Ⓔ
17. Ⓐ Ⓑ Ⓒ Ⓓ Ⓔ
18. Ⓐ Ⓑ Ⓒ Ⓓ Ⓔ
19. Ⓐ Ⓑ Ⓒ Ⓓ Ⓔ
20. Ⓐ Ⓑ Ⓒ Ⓓ Ⓔ

TEST 2: SENTENCE COMPLETION

S. Ⓐ Ⓑ Ⓒ Ⓓ Ⓔ
1. Ⓐ Ⓑ Ⓒ Ⓓ Ⓔ
2. Ⓐ Ⓑ Ⓒ Ⓓ Ⓔ
3. Ⓐ Ⓑ Ⓒ Ⓓ Ⓔ
4. Ⓐ Ⓑ Ⓒ Ⓓ Ⓔ
5. Ⓐ Ⓑ Ⓒ Ⓓ Ⓔ
6. Ⓐ Ⓑ Ⓒ Ⓓ Ⓔ
7. Ⓐ Ⓑ Ⓒ Ⓓ Ⓔ
8. Ⓐ Ⓑ Ⓒ Ⓓ Ⓔ
9. Ⓐ Ⓑ Ⓒ Ⓓ Ⓔ
10. Ⓐ Ⓑ Ⓒ Ⓓ Ⓔ
11. Ⓐ Ⓑ Ⓒ Ⓓ Ⓔ
12. Ⓐ Ⓑ Ⓒ Ⓓ Ⓔ
13. Ⓐ Ⓑ Ⓒ Ⓓ Ⓔ
14. Ⓐ Ⓑ Ⓒ Ⓓ Ⓔ
15. Ⓐ Ⓑ Ⓒ Ⓓ Ⓔ
16. Ⓐ Ⓑ Ⓒ Ⓓ Ⓔ
17. Ⓐ Ⓑ Ⓒ Ⓓ Ⓔ
18. Ⓐ Ⓑ Ⓒ Ⓓ Ⓔ
19. Ⓐ Ⓑ Ⓒ Ⓓ Ⓔ
20. Ⓐ Ⓑ Ⓒ Ⓓ Ⓔ

TEST 3: VERBAL ANALOGIES

S. Ⓐ Ⓑ Ⓒ Ⓓ Ⓔ
1. Ⓐ Ⓑ Ⓒ Ⓓ Ⓔ
2. Ⓐ Ⓑ Ⓒ Ⓓ Ⓔ
3. Ⓐ Ⓑ Ⓒ Ⓓ Ⓔ
4. Ⓐ Ⓑ Ⓒ Ⓓ Ⓔ
5. Ⓐ Ⓑ Ⓒ Ⓓ Ⓔ
6. Ⓐ Ⓑ Ⓒ Ⓓ Ⓔ
7. Ⓐ Ⓑ Ⓒ Ⓓ Ⓔ
8. Ⓐ Ⓑ Ⓒ Ⓓ Ⓔ
9. Ⓐ Ⓑ Ⓒ Ⓓ Ⓔ
10. Ⓐ Ⓑ Ⓒ Ⓓ Ⓔ
11. Ⓐ Ⓑ Ⓒ Ⓓ Ⓔ
12. Ⓐ Ⓑ Ⓒ Ⓓ Ⓔ
13. Ⓐ Ⓑ Ⓒ Ⓓ Ⓔ
14. Ⓐ Ⓑ Ⓒ Ⓓ Ⓔ
15. Ⓐ Ⓑ Ⓒ Ⓓ Ⓔ
16. Ⓐ Ⓑ Ⓒ Ⓓ Ⓔ
17. Ⓐ Ⓑ Ⓒ Ⓓ Ⓔ
18. Ⓐ Ⓑ Ⓒ Ⓓ Ⓔ
19. Ⓐ Ⓑ Ⓒ Ⓓ Ⓔ
20. Ⓐ Ⓑ Ⓒ Ⓓ Ⓔ
21. Ⓐ Ⓑ Ⓒ Ⓓ Ⓔ
22. Ⓐ Ⓑ Ⓒ Ⓓ Ⓔ
23. Ⓐ Ⓑ Ⓒ Ⓓ Ⓔ
24. Ⓐ Ⓑ Ⓒ Ⓓ Ⓔ
25. Ⓐ Ⓑ Ⓒ Ⓓ Ⓔ

CogAT® **Practice Test – Answer Sheets**   Bright Kids NYC Inc ©

QUANTITATIVE BATTERY

TEST 4: QUANTITATIVE RELATIONS

S. Ⓐ Ⓑ Ⓒ Ⓓ Ⓔ
1. Ⓐ Ⓑ Ⓒ Ⓓ Ⓔ
2. Ⓐ Ⓑ Ⓒ Ⓓ Ⓔ
3. Ⓐ Ⓑ Ⓒ Ⓓ Ⓔ
4. Ⓐ Ⓑ Ⓒ Ⓓ Ⓔ
5. Ⓐ Ⓑ Ⓒ Ⓓ Ⓔ
6. Ⓐ Ⓑ Ⓒ Ⓓ Ⓔ
7. Ⓐ Ⓑ Ⓒ Ⓓ Ⓔ
8. Ⓐ Ⓑ Ⓒ Ⓓ Ⓔ
9. Ⓐ Ⓑ Ⓒ Ⓓ Ⓔ
10. Ⓐ Ⓑ Ⓒ Ⓓ Ⓔ
11. Ⓐ Ⓑ Ⓒ Ⓓ Ⓔ
12. Ⓐ Ⓑ Ⓒ Ⓓ Ⓔ
13. Ⓐ Ⓑ Ⓒ Ⓓ Ⓔ
14. Ⓐ Ⓑ Ⓒ Ⓓ Ⓔ
15. Ⓐ Ⓑ Ⓒ Ⓓ Ⓔ
16. Ⓐ Ⓑ Ⓒ Ⓓ Ⓔ
17. Ⓐ Ⓑ Ⓒ Ⓓ Ⓔ
18. Ⓐ Ⓑ Ⓒ Ⓓ Ⓔ
19. Ⓐ Ⓑ Ⓒ Ⓓ Ⓔ
20. Ⓐ Ⓑ Ⓒ Ⓓ Ⓔ
21. Ⓐ Ⓑ Ⓒ Ⓓ Ⓔ
22. Ⓐ Ⓑ Ⓒ Ⓓ Ⓔ
23. Ⓐ Ⓑ Ⓒ Ⓓ Ⓔ
24. Ⓐ Ⓑ Ⓒ Ⓓ Ⓔ
25. Ⓐ Ⓑ Ⓒ Ⓓ Ⓔ

TEST 5: NUMBER SERIES

S. Ⓐ Ⓑ Ⓒ Ⓓ Ⓔ
1. Ⓐ Ⓑ Ⓒ Ⓓ Ⓔ
2. Ⓐ Ⓑ Ⓒ Ⓓ Ⓔ
3. Ⓐ Ⓑ Ⓒ Ⓓ Ⓔ
4. Ⓐ Ⓑ Ⓒ Ⓓ Ⓔ
5. Ⓐ Ⓑ Ⓒ Ⓓ Ⓔ
6. Ⓐ Ⓑ Ⓒ Ⓓ Ⓔ
7. Ⓐ Ⓑ Ⓒ Ⓓ Ⓔ
8. Ⓐ Ⓑ Ⓒ Ⓓ Ⓔ
9. Ⓐ Ⓑ Ⓒ Ⓓ Ⓔ
10. Ⓐ Ⓑ Ⓒ Ⓓ Ⓔ
11. Ⓐ Ⓑ Ⓒ Ⓓ Ⓔ
12. Ⓐ Ⓑ Ⓒ Ⓓ Ⓔ
13. Ⓐ Ⓑ Ⓒ Ⓓ Ⓔ
14. Ⓐ Ⓑ Ⓒ Ⓓ Ⓔ
15. Ⓐ Ⓑ Ⓒ Ⓓ Ⓔ
16. Ⓐ Ⓑ Ⓒ Ⓓ Ⓔ
17. Ⓐ Ⓑ Ⓒ Ⓓ Ⓔ
18. Ⓐ Ⓑ Ⓒ Ⓓ Ⓔ
19. Ⓐ Ⓑ Ⓒ Ⓓ Ⓔ
20. Ⓐ Ⓑ Ⓒ Ⓓ Ⓔ

TEST 6: EQUATION BUILDING

S. Ⓐ Ⓑ Ⓒ Ⓓ Ⓔ
1. Ⓐ Ⓑ Ⓒ Ⓓ Ⓔ
2. Ⓐ Ⓑ Ⓒ Ⓓ Ⓔ
3. Ⓐ Ⓑ Ⓒ Ⓓ Ⓔ
4. Ⓐ Ⓑ Ⓒ Ⓓ Ⓔ
5. Ⓐ Ⓑ Ⓒ Ⓓ Ⓔ
6. Ⓐ Ⓑ Ⓒ Ⓓ Ⓔ
7. Ⓐ Ⓑ Ⓒ Ⓓ Ⓔ
8. Ⓐ Ⓑ Ⓒ Ⓓ Ⓔ
9. Ⓐ Ⓑ Ⓒ Ⓓ Ⓔ
10. Ⓐ Ⓑ Ⓒ Ⓓ Ⓔ
11. Ⓐ Ⓑ Ⓒ Ⓓ Ⓔ
12. Ⓐ Ⓑ Ⓒ Ⓓ Ⓔ
13. Ⓐ Ⓑ Ⓒ Ⓓ Ⓔ
14. Ⓐ Ⓑ Ⓒ Ⓓ Ⓔ
15. Ⓐ Ⓑ Ⓒ Ⓓ Ⓔ

CogAT® Practice Test – Answer Sheets   Bright Kids NYC Inc ©

NONVERBAL BATTERY

TEST 7: FIGURE CLASSIFICATION

S. Ⓐ Ⓑ Ⓒ Ⓓ Ⓔ
1. Ⓐ Ⓑ Ⓒ Ⓓ Ⓔ
2. Ⓐ Ⓑ Ⓒ Ⓓ Ⓔ
3. Ⓐ Ⓑ Ⓒ Ⓓ Ⓔ
4. Ⓐ Ⓑ Ⓒ Ⓓ Ⓔ
5. Ⓐ Ⓑ Ⓒ Ⓓ Ⓔ
6. Ⓐ Ⓑ Ⓒ Ⓓ Ⓔ
7. Ⓐ Ⓑ Ⓒ Ⓓ Ⓔ
8. Ⓐ Ⓑ Ⓒ Ⓓ Ⓔ
9. Ⓐ Ⓑ Ⓒ Ⓓ Ⓔ
10. Ⓐ Ⓑ Ⓒ Ⓓ Ⓔ
11. Ⓐ Ⓑ Ⓒ Ⓓ Ⓔ
12. Ⓐ Ⓑ Ⓒ Ⓓ Ⓔ
13. Ⓐ Ⓑ Ⓒ Ⓓ Ⓔ
14. Ⓐ Ⓑ Ⓒ Ⓓ Ⓔ
15. Ⓐ Ⓑ Ⓒ Ⓓ Ⓔ
16. Ⓐ Ⓑ Ⓒ Ⓓ Ⓔ
17. Ⓐ Ⓑ Ⓒ Ⓓ Ⓔ
18. Ⓐ Ⓑ Ⓒ Ⓓ Ⓔ
19. Ⓐ Ⓑ Ⓒ Ⓓ Ⓔ
20. Ⓐ Ⓑ Ⓒ Ⓓ Ⓔ
21. Ⓐ Ⓑ Ⓒ Ⓓ Ⓔ
22. Ⓐ Ⓑ Ⓒ Ⓓ Ⓔ
23. Ⓐ Ⓑ Ⓒ Ⓓ Ⓔ
24. Ⓐ Ⓑ Ⓒ Ⓓ Ⓔ
25. Ⓐ Ⓑ Ⓒ Ⓓ Ⓔ

TEST 8: FIGURE ANALOGIES

S. Ⓐ Ⓑ Ⓒ Ⓓ Ⓔ
1. Ⓐ Ⓑ Ⓒ Ⓓ Ⓔ
2. Ⓐ Ⓑ Ⓒ Ⓓ Ⓔ
3. Ⓐ Ⓑ Ⓒ Ⓓ Ⓔ
4. Ⓐ Ⓑ Ⓒ Ⓓ Ⓔ
5. Ⓐ Ⓑ Ⓒ Ⓓ Ⓔ
6. Ⓐ Ⓑ Ⓒ Ⓓ Ⓔ
7. Ⓐ Ⓑ Ⓒ Ⓓ Ⓔ
8. Ⓐ Ⓑ Ⓒ Ⓓ Ⓔ
9. Ⓐ Ⓑ Ⓒ Ⓓ Ⓔ
10. Ⓐ Ⓑ Ⓒ Ⓓ Ⓔ
11. Ⓐ Ⓑ Ⓒ Ⓓ Ⓔ
12. Ⓐ Ⓑ Ⓒ Ⓓ Ⓔ
13. Ⓐ Ⓑ Ⓒ Ⓓ Ⓔ
14. Ⓐ Ⓑ Ⓒ Ⓓ Ⓔ
15. Ⓐ Ⓑ Ⓒ Ⓓ Ⓔ
16. Ⓐ Ⓑ Ⓒ Ⓓ Ⓔ
17. Ⓐ Ⓑ Ⓒ Ⓓ Ⓔ
18. Ⓐ Ⓑ Ⓒ Ⓓ Ⓔ
19. Ⓐ Ⓑ Ⓒ Ⓓ Ⓔ
20. Ⓐ Ⓑ Ⓒ Ⓓ Ⓔ
21. Ⓐ Ⓑ Ⓒ Ⓓ Ⓔ
22. Ⓐ Ⓑ Ⓒ Ⓓ Ⓔ
23. Ⓐ Ⓑ Ⓒ Ⓓ Ⓔ
24. Ⓐ Ⓑ Ⓒ Ⓓ Ⓔ
25. Ⓐ Ⓑ Ⓒ Ⓓ Ⓔ

TEST 9: FIGURE ANALYSIS

S. Ⓐ Ⓑ Ⓒ Ⓓ Ⓔ
1. Ⓐ Ⓑ Ⓒ Ⓓ Ⓔ
2. Ⓐ Ⓑ Ⓒ Ⓓ Ⓔ
3. Ⓐ Ⓑ Ⓒ Ⓓ Ⓔ
4. Ⓐ Ⓑ Ⓒ Ⓓ Ⓔ
5. Ⓐ Ⓑ Ⓒ Ⓓ Ⓔ
6. Ⓐ Ⓑ Ⓒ Ⓓ Ⓔ
7. Ⓐ Ⓑ Ⓒ Ⓓ Ⓔ
8. Ⓐ Ⓑ Ⓒ Ⓓ Ⓔ
9. Ⓐ Ⓑ Ⓒ Ⓓ Ⓔ
10. Ⓐ Ⓑ Ⓒ Ⓓ Ⓔ
11. Ⓐ Ⓑ Ⓒ Ⓓ Ⓔ
12. Ⓐ Ⓑ Ⓒ Ⓓ Ⓔ
13. Ⓐ Ⓑ Ⓒ Ⓓ Ⓔ
14. Ⓐ Ⓑ Ⓒ Ⓓ Ⓔ
15. Ⓐ Ⓑ Ⓒ Ⓓ Ⓔ

CogAT® Practice Test – Answer Sheets

Bright Kids NYC Inc ©